THE LITTLE GOLDEN
MOTHER GOOSE

ILLUSTRATED BY FEODOR ROJANKOVSKY

GOLDEN PRESS
Western Publishing Company, Inc.
Racine, Wisconsin

HOW MANY MILES TO BABYLON?

How many miles to Babylon?
Threescore miles and ten.
Can I get there by candlelight?
Yes, and back again.
If your heels are nimble and light,
You may get there by candlelight.

THE SEASONS

Spring is showery, flowery, bowery;
Summer: hoppy, croppy, poppy;
Autumn: wheezy, sneezy, freezy;
Winter: slippy, drippy, nippy.

Eighteenth Printing, 1980

SING A SONG OF SIXPENCE

Sing a song of sixpence,
A pocket full of rye;
Four-and-twenty blackbirds
Baked in a pie.
When the pie was opened
The birds began to sing;
Wasn't that a dainty dish
To set before the King?

The King was in the countinghouse,
Counting out his money;
The Queen was in the parlor,
Eating bread and honey.
The maid was in the garden,
Hanging out the clothes;
When down came a blackbird
And snipped off her nose.

OLD MOTHER GOOSE

Old Mother Goose, when
She wanted to wander,
Would ride through the air
On a very fine gander.

GOOSEY, GOOSEY, GANDER

Goosey, goosey, gander,
Whither shall I wander?
Upstairs and downstairs,
And in my lady's chamber.

IF WISHES WERE HORSES

If wishes were horses,
Beggars would ride;
If turnips were watches,
I'd wear one by my side.

JACK SPRAT

Jack Sprat could eat no fat,
His wife could eat no lean,
And so between them both,
They licked the platter clean.

LEG OVER LEG

Leg over leg,
As the dog went to Dover;
When he came to a stile
Hop! he went over.

GEORGIE PORGIE

Georgie Porgie, pudding and pie,
Kissed the girls and made them cry;
When the boys came out to play,
Georgie Porgie ran away.

HARK! HARK!

Hark! Hark! The dogs do bark,
Beggars are coming to town;
Some in rags and some in tags,
And some in velvet gowns.

LITTLE TOMMY TITTLEMOUSE

Little Tommy Tittlemouse
Lived in a little house;
He caught fishes
In other men's ditches.

LUCY LOCKET

Lucy Locket lost her pocket,
Kitty Fisher found it;
There was not a penny in it,
But a ribbon round it.

BYE, BABY BUNTING

Bye, baby bunting,
Daddy's gone a-hunting,
To get a little rabbit's skin
To wrap his baby bunting in.

MISTRESS MARY

Mistress Mary, quite contrary,
How does your garden grow?
With cockle shells and silver bells
And pretty maids all in a row.

PETER, PETER

Peter, Peter, pumpkin eater,
Had a wife and couldn't keep her;
He put her in a pumpkin shell,
And there he kept her very well.

HANDY SPANDY

Handy Spandy, Jack-a-dandy,
Loves plum cake and sugar candy.
He bought some at the grocer's shop
And out he came, hop, hop, hop!

RING A RING O' ROSES

Ring a ring o' roses,
A pocket full of posies.
Tisha! Tisha!
We all fall down.

THREE WISE MEN OF GOTHAM

Three wise men of Gotham
Went to sea in a bowl;
If the bowl had been stronger,
My story would have been longer.

GRAY GOOSE AND GRAY GANDER

Gray goose and gray gander,
Waft your wings together
And carry the good king's daughter
Over the one-strand river.

PLAY DAYS

How many days has my baby to play?
Saturday, Sunday, Monday,
Tuesday, Wednesday, Thursday, Friday,
Saturday, Sunday, Monday.

DEEDLE, DEEDLE, DUMPLING

Deedle, deedle, dumpling, my son John,
He went to bed with his stockings on;
One shoe off, and one shoe on;
Deedle, deedle, dumpling, my son John.

TO MARKET, TO MARKET

To market, to market to buy a fat pig,
Home again, home again, jiggety-jig;
To market, to market to buy a fat hog,
Home again, home again, jiggety-jog.

SEE-SAW, MARGERY DAW

See-saw, Margery Daw,
Jacky shall have a new master;
He shall have but a penny a day,
Because he can't work any faster.

HOT-CROSS BUNS!

Hot-cross buns! Hot-cross buns!
One a penny, two a penny, hot-cross buns.
If you have no daughters, give them to your sons.
One a penny, two a penny, hot-cross buns.

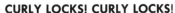

CURLY LOCKS! CURLY LOCKS!

Curly Locks! Curly Locks! wilt thou be mine?
Thou shalt not wash dishes, nor yet feed the swine;
But sit on a cushion, and sew a fine seam,
And feed upon strawberries, sugar and cream!

HUMPTY DUMPTY

Humpty Dumpty sat on a wall,
Humpty Dumpty had a great fall;
All the King's horses and all the King's men
Cannot put Humpty Dumpty together again.

PAT-A-CAKE

Pat-a-cake, pat-a-cake, baker's man!
Bake me a cake as fast as you can;
Roll it and pat it and mark it with "B,"
And put it in the oven for baby and me.

LITTLE BO-PEEP HAS LOST HER SHEEP

Little Bo-peep has lost her sheep,
And can't tell where to find them;
Leave them alone, and they'll come home,
And bring their tails behind them.

LITTLE JACK HORNER

Little Jack Horner sat in the corner,
Eating a Christmas pie;
He put in his thumb, and he pulled out a plum,
And said, "What a good boy am I!"

TO BED, TO BED!

"To bed, to bed!" says Sleepy-head.
"Tarry awhile," says Slow.
"Put on the pan," says greedy Nan.
"We'll sup before we go."

THERE WAS A CROOKED MAN

There was a crooked man, and he went a crooked mile,
He found a crooked sixpence against a crooked stile;
He bought a crooked cat, which caught a crooked mouse,
And they all lived together in a little crooked house.

BAA, BAA, BLACK SHEEP

Baa, baa, black sheep, have you any wool?
Yes, sir, yes, sir, three bags full:
One for my master, one for my dame,
And one for the little boy that lives in our lane.

LADYBIRD!

Ladybird! Ladybird! fly away home;
Your house is on fire, your children all gone;
All but one, and her name is Ann,
And she crept under the pudding pan.

SIMPLE SIMON

Simple Simon met a pieman, going to the fair;
Says Simple Simon to the pieman, "Let me taste your ware."
Says the pieman to Simple Simon, "Show me first your penny."
Says Simple Simon to the pieman, "Indeed I have not any."

WILLY BOY

"Willy Boy, Willy Boy, where are you going?
I will go with you, if that I may."
"I'm going to the meadow to see them a-mowing,
I'm going to help them make the hay."

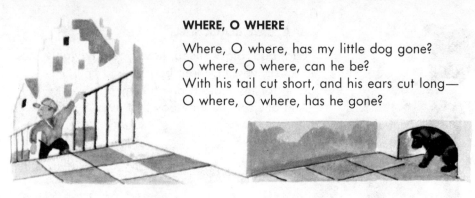

WHERE, O WHERE

Where, O where, has my little dog gone?
O where, O where, can he be?
With his tail cut short, and his ears cut long—
O where, O where, has he gone?

THE LITTLE GIRL WITH THE CURL

There was a little girl, who had a little curl
Right in the middle of her forehead;
When she was good she was very, very good
But when she was bad she was horrid.

THE OLD WOMAN IN THE SHOE

There was an old woman who lived in a shoe.
She had so many children she didn't know what to do.
She gave them some broth, without any bread,
And whipped them all soundly, and sent them to bed.

WEE WILLIE WINKIE

Wee Willie Winkie runs through the town,
Upstairs and downstairs, in his nightgown;
Rapping at the window, crying through the lock,
"Are the children in their beds? Now it's eight o'clock."

PETER PIPER

Peter Piper picked a peck of pickled peppers;
A peck of pickled peppers Peter Piper picked.
If Peter Piper picked a peck of pickled peppers,
Where's the peck of pickled peppers Peter Piper picked?

LONDON BRIDGE

London Bridge is falling down,
Falling down, falling down.
London Bridge is falling down,
My fair lady.

THE COCK'S ON THE HOUSETOP

The cock's on the housetop blowing his horn;
The bull's in the barn a-threshing of corn;
The maids in the meadows are making of hay;
The ducks in the river are swimming away.

AS I WAS GOING TO ST. IVES

As I was going to St. Ives,
I met a man with seven wives.
Every wife had seven sacks,
Every sack had seven cats,
Every cat had seven kits.
Kits, cats, sacks and wives,
How many were going to St. Ives?

JACK AND JILL

Jack and Jill went up the hill
To fetch a pail of water;
Jack fell down and broke his crown,
And Jill came tumbling after.

Then up Jack got, and home did trot,
As fast as he could caper.
They put him to bed and plastered his head
With vinegar and brown paper.

PUSSY CAT, PUSSY CAT

"Pussy Cat, Pussy Cat,
Where have you been?"
"I've been to London
To look at the Queen."

"Pussy Cat, Pussy Cat,
What did you there?"
"I frightened a little mouse
Under the chair."

PEASE PORRIDGE HOT

Pease porridge hot,
Pease porridge cold,
Pease porridge in the pot,
Nine days old.

Some like it hot,
Some like it cold,
Some like it in the pot,
Nine days old.

I HAD A LITTLE PONY

I had a little pony,
His name was Dapple-Gray;
I lent him to a lady
To ride a mile away.

She whipped him, she slashed him,
She rode him through the mire;
I would not lend my pony now
For all the lady's hire.

THE NORTH WIND

The north wind doth blow,
And we shall have snow,
And what will the robin do then,
   Poor thing?

He'll sit in the barn
And keep himself warm,
And hide his head under his wing,
   Poor thing!

RIDE A COCK-HORSE

Ride a cock-horse to Banbury Cross,
To see an old lady upon a white horse;
Rings on her fingers and bells on her toes,
She shall have music wherever she goes.

Ride a cock-horse to Banbury Cross,
To see what Tommy can buy.
A penny white loaf, a penny white cake,
And a two-penny apple pie!

LITTLE TOMMY TUCKER

Little Tommy Tucker
Sings for his supper.
What shall he eat?
White bread and butter.

How will he cut it
Without e'er a knife?
How can he marry
Without e'er a wife?

BOBBY SHAFTOE

Bobby Shaftoe's gone to sea,
Silver buckles on his knee;
He'll come back and marry me,
Pretty Bobby Shaftoe.

Bobby Shaftoe's fat and fair,
Combing down his yellow hair;
He's my love forevermore,
Pretty Bobby Shaftoe.

POLLY, PUT THE KETTLE ON

Polly, put the kettle on,
Polly, put the kettle on,
Polly, put the kettle on,
We'll all have tea.

Sukey, take it off again,
Sukey, take it off again,
Sukey, take it off again,
They've all gone away.

WHAT ARE LITTLE BOYS MADE OF?

What are little boys made of, made of?
What are little boys made of?
Frogs and snails, and puppy-dogs' tails,
That's what little boys are made of.

What are little girls made of, made of?
What are little girls made of?
Sugar and spice, and all that's nice;
That's what little girls are made of.

TOM, TOM, THE PIPER'S SON

Tom, Tom, the piper's son,
Stole a pig and away he run.
The pig was eat and Tom was beat,
And Tom went crying down the street.

Tom, Tom, the piper's son,
He learned to play when he was young;
But all the tunes that he could play
Was "Over the hills and far away."

THE LITTLE BIRD

Once I saw a little bird
Come hop, hop, hop;
So I cried, "Little bird,
Will you stop, stop, stop?"

And was going to the window
To say, "How do you do?"
But he shook his little tail
And far away he flew.

THE QUEEN OF HEARTS

The Queen of Hearts,
She made some tarts,
All on a summer's day.
The Knave of Hearts,
He stole the tarts,
And took them clean away.

The King of Hearts
Called for the tarts,
And beat the Knave full sore.
The Knave of Hearts
Brought back the tarts,
And vowed he'd steal no more.

JACK, BE NIMBLE

Jack, be nimble,
Jack, be quick,
Jack, jump over the candlestick.

DAFFY-DOWN-DILLY

Daffy-down-dilly has come up to town
In a yellow petticoat and a green gown.

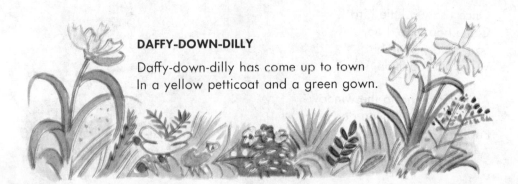

LITTLE ROBIN REDBREAST

Little Robin Redbreast sat upon a rail;
Niddle-naddle went his head, wiggle-waggle went his tail.

Little Robin Redbreast sat upon a tree,
Up went Pussy Cat, and down went he.

Down came Pussy Cat, and away Robin ran;
Says little Robin Redbreast, "Catch me if you can."

Little Robin Redbreast jumped upon a wall;
Pussy Cat jumped after him, and almost got a fall.

Little Robin chirped and sang, and what did Pussy say?
Pussy Cat said, "Mew," and Robin jumped away.

TWO LITTLE DOGS

Two little dogs
Sat by the fire,
Over a fender of coal-dust;
Said one little dog
To the other little dog,
"If you don't talk, why, I must."

RUB-A-DUB-DUB

Rub-a-dub-dub,
Three men in a tub;
And who do you think they be?
The butcher, the baker,
The candlestick-maker;
Turn 'em out, knaves all three!

A CAT CAME FIDDLING

A cat came fiddling out of a barn,
With a pair of bagpipes under her arm;
She could sing nothing but fiddle-de-dee,
The mouse has married the bumblebee;
Pipe, cat; dance, mouse—
We'll have a wedding at our good house.

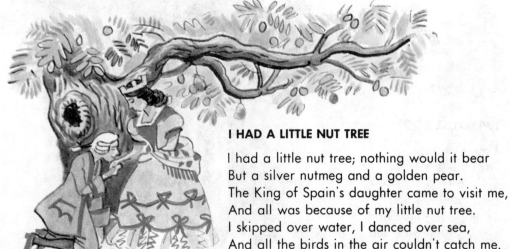

I HAD A LITTLE NUT TREE

I had a little nut tree; nothing would it bear
But a silver nutmeg and a golden pear.
The King of Spain's daughter came to visit me,
And all was because of my little nut tree.
I skipped over water, I danced over sea,
And all the birds in the air couldn't catch me.

LITTLE POLL PARROT

Little Poll Parrot
Sat in a garret,
Eating toast and tea;
A little brown mouse
Jumped into the house
And took it all away.

THIS LITTLE PIG

This little pig went to market;
This little pig stayed at home;
This little pig had roast beef;
This little pig had none;
This little pig said, "Wee, wee, wee!"
All the way home.

MY LITTLE HEN

I had a little hen, the prettiest ever seen,
She washed me the dishes and kept the house clean;
She went to the mill to fetch me some flour;
She brought it home in less than an hour;
She baked me my bread, she brewed me my ale;
She sat by the fire and told many a fine tale.

OLD KING COLE

Old King Cole was a merry old soul,
And a merry old soul was he.
He called for his pipe,
He called for his bowl,
And he called for his fiddlers three.

A DILLAR, A DOLLAR

A dillar, a dollar,
A ten-o'clock scholar,
What makes you come so soon?
You used to come at ten o'clock,
And now you come at noon.

THE CAT AND THE FIDDLE

Hey, diddle, diddle!
The cat and the fiddle,
The cow jumped over the moon;
The little dog laughed to see such sport,
And the dish ran away with the spoon.

HICKORY, DICKORY

Hickory, dickory, dock,
The mouse ran up the clock;
The clock struck one,
And down he run,
Hickory, dickory, dock.

OLD MOTHER HUBBARD

Old Mother Hubbard
Went to the cupboard,
To get her poor dog a bone;
When she got there
The cupboard was bare,
And so the poor dog had none.

I LOVE LITTLE PUSSY

I love little pussy, her coat is so warm,
And if I don't hurt her, she'll do me no harm.
So I'll not pull her tail, nor drive her away,
But pussy and I very gently will play.
I'll sit by the fire, and give her some food,
And pussy will love me because I am good.

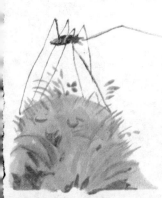

LITTLE MISS MUFFET

Little Miss Muffet
She sat on a tuffet,
Eating of curds and whey;
There came a great spider,
Who sat down beside her,
And frightened Miss Muffet away.

DING, DONG BELL!

Ding, dong, bell!
Pussy's in the well!
Who put her in?
Little Johnny Green.
Who pulled her out?
Little Johnny Stout.

What a naughty boy was that,
To try to drown poor pussy cat,
Which never did him any harm,
But killed the mice in his father's barn!

TWO BLACKBIRDS

There were two blackbirds,
Sitting on a hill,
The one named Jack,
The other named Jill;
Fly away, Jack! Fly away, Jill!
Come again, Jack! Come again, Jill!